Classic Tales

Level 1

The Lazy Grasshopper

Retold by Rachel Bladon
Illustrated by Bruno Robert

Contents

OXFORD
UNIVERSITY PRESS

It's summer, and it's hot. The grasshopper sits in the shade and sings.

'What a beautiful day!' says Grasshopper.

2

What are you doing, Ant?

Grasshopper sees an ant.
She's carrying some food.

'What are you doing, Ant?'
says Grasshopper.

'I'm carrying food to my home,'
says Ant.

'It's very hot,' says Grasshopper.
'Come and sit down!
Have a cold drink!'

'No, thank you,' says Ant.
'I'm working. I'm making
a food store for the winter.'

Come and sit down!

'Winter!' Grasshopper laughs. 'Don't think about the winter!'

But Ant doesn't stop.

All day, Ant works. She carries food to her store. Then she goes and gets some more. She's hot and tired, but she doesn't stop.

Grasshopper sits in the shade.
He sings and sleeps all day.

'Silly Ant!' he laughs. 'Don't think
about your winter store. Look at
me! When I'm hungry, I eat some
berries or a nice leaf.'

All summer the ant works.

'Come and sit down!' Grasshopper says to her every day.

'No, thank you,' says Ant.
'I must make my winter store.'

All summer Grasshopper sits
in the shade. He sings and sleeps,
and he eats berries and leaves.

It's autumn now, and it rains every day. Grasshopper sits in a tree.

He sees Ant. She's carrying food.

'Come and sit here with me!' Grasshopper says. 'It's dry here!'

'No, thank you,' says Ant. 'I'm making a store for the winter.'

'Winter!' says Grasshopper. 'Don't think about the winter!'

But Ant doesn't stop. She works all day. She carries food to her store, and then she goes and gets some more.

'Silly Ant,' Grasshopper laughs. 'Don't think about your winter store. Look at me! When I'm hungry, I eat some berries or a nice leaf.'

All autumn the ant works.

'Come and sit here with me!'
Grasshopper says to her every day.

'No, thank you,' says Ant.
'I must make my winter store.'

All autumn Grasshopper sits in the tree. It's dry here. There aren't many leaves and berries, but every day he finds one or two.

It's cold now, and snow comes.
Grasshopper sits under a rock.

He sees Ant. She's carrying food.

'Come and sit here with me!'
Grasshopper says to Ant.
'It's warmer here!'

It's warmer here!

Ant stops.

'No, thank you,' she says. 'I'm going to my home. My store is full, and now I can stay at home all winter!'

'Oh,' says Grasshopper.
'So it's winter now?'

'Yes,' says Ant.
'Goodbye, Grasshopper.'

Goodbye, Grasshopper.

Grasshopper sits under the rock.
It's cold. Very cold. There are no
berries. No berries and only one
or two leaves.

All day Grasshopper sits under the rock. He's hungry and cold.

'Ant is my friend!' he says. 'She has a big winter store. She can give me some food.'

So he goes to Ant's home.

Ant is my friend!

Ant's home is warm, and there's lots of food.

'Hello, Ant,' Grasshopper says. 'There are no berries now, but you have a big winter store. Please give me some food.'

'I'm sorry, Grasshopper,' says Ant. 'This is my winter store. I have to eat this food all winter. I can't give you any food. Goodbye.'

Please give me some food.

I'm sorry, Grasshopper.

'Clever Ant,' Grasshopper says.
'She works all year, and now she has
lots of food. Look at me! I sing and
sleep all year, and now I'm hungry.
Silly me. Silly Grasshopper!'

And the grasshopper walks home
to his rock, cold and hungry.

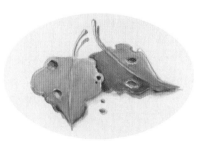

1 Write the words.

It's a <u>rock</u>.

It's a _____.

It's a _____.

It's an _____.

They're _____.

It's _____.

2 Write the words.

berries   full   rock   ~~shade~~   store

1 All summer Grasshopper sits in the <u>*shade*</u>.

2 When Grasshopper is hungry, he eats _____ or a nice leaf.

3 Ant carries food to her _____ all day.

4 In the winter, Grasshopper sits under a _____.

5 Ant can stay at home in the winter because her store is _____.

3 Make sentences about the story.

Grasshopper

Ant

sits in the shade all summer.
works all year.
makes a food store.
sits in a tree all autumn.
is hungry in the winter.
stays at home in the winter.

1 *Grasshopper sits in the shade all summer.*
2 _____
3 _____
4 _____
5 _____
6 _____

4 Answer the questions.

1 Who's this? *It's Grasshopper.*   3 Is he cold? _____
2 Is he clever? _____   4 Is he hungry? _____

1 Who's this?

  _____

2 Is she warm?

  _____

3 Is she silly?

  _____

Picture Dictionary

autumn *It's autumn.*

food

berries

full *It's full.*

carry

laugh

clever *She's clever.*

leaf

dry *It's dry.*

lots of *lots of ants*

rock

store

shade

summer *It's summer.*

silly *He's silly.*

tree

sing

under *under a rock*

snow

warm *It's warm.*

stay *stay at home*

winter *It's winter.*

Classic Tales

Classic stories retold for learners of English – bringing the magic of traditional storytelling to the language classroom

For Classic Tales Teacher's Handbook, visit www.oup.com/elt/readers/classictales

Level 1: 100 headwords
- The Enormous Turnip
- The Lazy Grasshopper
- The Little Red Hen
- Lownu Mends the Sky
- The Magic Cooking Pot
- The Magpie and the Milk
- Mansour and the Donkey
- Peach Boy
- The Princess and the Pea
- Rumpelstiltskin
- The Shoemaker and the Elves
- Three Billy-Goats

Level 2: 150 headwords
- Amrita and the Trees
- Big Baby Finn
- The Fisherman and his Wife
- The Gingerbread Man
- Jack and the Beanstalk
- King Arthur and the Sword
- Rainforest Boy
- Thumbelina
- The Town Mouse and the Country Mouse
- The Ugly Duckling

Level 3: 200 headwords
- Aladdin
- Bambi and the Prince of the Forest
- Goldilocks and the Three Bears
- The Heron and the Hummingbird
- The Little Mermaid
- Little Red Riding Hood
- Rapunzel

Level 4: 300 headwords
- Cinderella
- Don Quixote: Adventures of a Spanish Knight
- The Goose Girl
- Sleeping Beauty
- The Twelve Dancing Princesses

Level 5: 400 headwords
- Beauty and the Beast
- The Magic Brocade
- Pinocchio
- Snow White and the Seven Dwarfs

OXFORD
UNIVERSITY PRESS

Great Clarendon Street, Oxford, OX2 6DP, United Kingdom

Oxford University Press is a department of the University of Oxford. It furthers the University's objective of excellence in research, scholarship, and education by publishing worldwide. Oxford is a registered trade mark of Oxford University Press in the UK and in certain other countries

© Oxford University Press 2014

The moral rights of the author have been asserted

First published in 2014

2023

21

ISBN: 978 0 19 423981 3   Book
ISBN: 978 0 19 410802 7   e-Book
ISBN: 978 0 19 423987 5   Activity Book and Play
ISBN: 978 0 19 400423 7   Audio Pack

Printed in China

This book is printed on paper from certified and well-managed sources

ACKNOWLEDGEMENTS

Illustrated by: Bruno Robert / Plum Pudding Illustration